One day Harpo is sleeping in the mud at the edge of the river.

Alfie is in the river. He is splashing

water all over himself.

Suddenly Alfie sees a big crocodile go into the water.

'Harpo, Harpo,' he shouts. 'A big crocodile is in the river. Get out quickly.'

Harpo jumps up. He tries to get out of the mud quickly, but he slips.

Alfie rushes to help Harpo. He pushes
him until he can stand up.

The two friends go up the riverbank to get away from the crocodile.

They sit at the top of the riverbank
and watch the crocodile swim past.